# The Illusionists

| | | |
|---|---|---|
| CA 14. SEP. 1982 | QC | QC |
| CA 26. APR. 1983 | CARTERTON 21 SEP 1981 | |
| AB ABINGDON | 02 MAY 1987 | |
| T.L. 11/86 | | |
| 16 DEC | | |

To renew, please quote these details and the number above the barcode

This book is due for return on or before the last date shown above. It may be renewed at the Library or by post or telephone.

**OXFORDSHIRE COUNTY LIBRARIES**

# The Illusionists

## A TALE

## *John Fuller*

Secker & Warburg
London

First published in England 1980 by
Martin Secker & Warburg Limited
54 Poland Street, London W1V 3DF

SBN: 436 16810 3

Filmset by Willmer Brothers Limited
Birkenhead, Merseyside
Printed and bound in Great Britain by
Biddles Ltd, Guildford and King's Lynn

# CONTENTS

# CHAPTER ONE

## ❧ The Beginning ❧

A man that has been brought up in ease and affluence, if he is of a quiet indolent nature, learns to shun everything that is troublesome, and chooses to curb his passions, more because of the inconveniences that arise from the eager pursuit after pleasure, and the yielding to all the demands of our inclinations, than any dislike he has to sensual enjoyments——
*Mandeville.*

## 1

Experience is an easy master,
Easy to stall–though not to fool:
However fast you go, he's faster.
He's there in front of you. Each rule
Is made by him. Relax! For living
On terms like his needs no forgiving.
Once we received with open hands
The *faits accomplis* of our glands,
And that's why no one ever changes:
The choice of being shy or wild
Is forced upon you as a child.
It's something that the womb arranges
(If not the womb, the family–
At least before the age of three).

## 2

Does mathematics make you weary?
I can't resist a simile
Drawn from a fairly useful theory
(Since similes should make you see
What otherwise is just asserted,
So that your judgement is exerted).
The gnomon is a constant: where
L shapes are added to a square
That square remains the same. A Roman
Is always more or less at home,
A Celt is still a Celt at Rome,
And all experience a gnomon.
From character there's no escape:
Experience can't change its shape.

And so our life stays in proportion—
Although experience extends
The ways we feel its deft contortion
Of all new means to the old ends:
The Presidential Lunch Companion
Whose hunger rivals the Grand Canyon
(Public, permanent and deep,
A national property, not cheap)
Was once a tot who showed her knickers
To catch an absent father's eye;
Bishops were babies who were shy
(The windy ones turn into vicars);
And those who liked to crawl in dirt
Invent machinery to hurt.

Tim as a child was quiet and stable.
He dressed up in his mother's skirts
Or played with flour beneath a table.
He bellowed mildly at his hurts
And sometimes tidied up his messes.
When he was told he formed his s's
Not with a curl but with a bend,
He blushed and promised he would mend.
You'd think that adults would be worried
By children happy on their own,
Who don't know better till they've grown,
But parents sometimes don't seem hurried
To finish work that's half-begun
And remedy an only son.

## 5

It wasn't very much to sigh at,
Nothing to make a boy complain,
Simply a dozen years of quiet,
Stagnation of the blood and brain.
Nothing there was he ever wanted
That wasn't immediately granted.
Such honeyed treatment has its sting:
He never wanted anything.
No siblings whom he could confide in
Challenged his private universe:
No elder sister like a nurse
With naughty secrets he could hide in,
No younger brother in his care
With whom he had to fight or share.

## 6

His father wasn't over-reckless.
When gilts were low he kept his head.
Mother inclined to wear a necklace,
Although she cooked and made the bed.
Tim came to learn they were not upper
By things like when they ate their supper.
Yet on that scale they were not low:
A comfortable fact to know.
Treated indeed by his relations
In those pecuniary ways
Which liven dull school holidays
(And, later on, the long vacations)
He felt that money grew for him
If not on trees, then at his whim.

At school he could not stand correction.
He found the swimming-bath too cold
And played for truces and protection
By reading Joyce at twelve years old
While chasing round with those much younger
And owning an immodest hunger
For every well-loved master's praise
(Reserving, though, the right to laze).
Later, the need for approbation
Made him excessively polite:
He never disagreed, despite
An urge to shock which sublimation
Converted to a milder trait
Of clamming up when *tête-à-tête*.

You know the sort—who treat a question
As though you aimed to catch them out,
As though it gave them indigestion
To be in any sort of doubt,
Who guard the cleavage of their answer
As close as a retired fan-dancer:
Smiles are the flowers of their talk,
Cool and reserved, with lots of stalk.
They do not mean to be mysterious
And haven't very much to hide.
Their silences are due to pride,
The need to seem relaxed and serious
When all the time they're scared as hell
You'll nail them with a *J'en appelle*.

## 9

The gnomon works. Those layers of living
Accumulate towards the grave.
Our naked selves are unforgiving
As they grow tall and learn to shave,
Are visited by mild afflictions,
Toothache and sex and social fictions,
Carrying keys or diaphragms,
Taking soft drugs or hard exams.
Beneath it all our Shape still trembles,
Unchanged by the absurd disguise
Of what we do to it. Its eyes
Stare dumbly out and it resembles
Nothing so much as a caged beast,
A butchered Banquo at the feast.

## 10

You'll say this story lacks coherence:
It hasn't got a sense of place,
Tim has no physical appearance.
What are his clothes like? Or his face?
The social background's pretty hazy.
Is it the poet being lazy
Or is it that he doesn't care?
Are there no facts that he can spare?
I must insist the poet retails
Only the goods he wants to stock.
Go to life's warehouse to unlock
That gloomy inventory of details
You need to validate the truth:
Put down the book and hire a sleuth.

## 11

If you're still with me, here's a label
It's possible to stick on Tim
(Try just a little, if you're able,
To close your eyes and picture him):
You'll find him aged nineteen at Camford
With his rough edges smoothed and chamfered,
Hair lying longer on his skull,
Silent still, but much less dull.
An undergraduate! That's better,
For few of them can seem miscast
When you enquire into their past.
All are free spirits to the letter.
Like workers threatening to strike
Or Chinamen, they're all alike.

## 12

I tease? Of course, but don't you tend to
Refer to groups and types like these?
And are ashamed? And then pretend to
A quizzical mock journalese?
Pity the foot-loose processed student:
The mind says ''should'', but money ''shouldn't'',
And then whatever he does well,
Odds on it's something he can't sell.
No wonder in studio or scrimmage,
In Castro beard or ancient car,
With racquet, fur-coat and guitar,
He seeks to fix the witless image
Created for him by the press.
It makes him feel he's a success.

## 13

Tim wasn't quite like this. I'm sorry
If I misled you, hampered your
Half-hearted chase after your quarry
With such a trivial hackneyed spoor.
The truth is that the hunt dismays me.
I need perspective, but it pays me
To keep a field or two ahead,
A brace of stanzas still unread.
I hear the breathing of the reader
As slow and heavy as a snore
But close, like steps outside a door.
It is a game of follow-my-leader?
And are there prizes in the race?
Charades, perhaps? A paper-chase?

## 14

Ah, yes. I scatter and you follow.
The scraps are quickly scanned and gone,
Like secret messages spies swallow
Or Christmas bangs with riddles on.
My story's somewhere, don't you doubt it:
How could I keep things up without it?
The many roots, the single trunk;
The separate scratchings of a monk
That slowly lend illumination;
The shifting of one's little stock
When playing patience round the clock;
Industrial negotiation:
Most steady purposes bespeak
A sometimes circular technique.

Now Tim had left his latest lecture
With notes upon *les Symbolises*
Idly scrawled as in a deckchair
Upon the outside of a creased
And second letter from his mother
Which asked why he'd ignored the other,
Now sandwiched in his copy of
*The Student's ABZ of Love*.
Though he was reading Modern Languages
The proper study of mankind
Is—woman. Tutors must not mind,
With such a rival, if work languishes:
Why slave to clear up others' doubt
Of what *their* lives were all about?

But still, if art v. life's in question,
A questionable gulf remained,
For youth is open to suggestion,
To literature's ideals enchained.
Frowning, in beads, with sheepish jerkin
(A Hobbit's view of Rupert Birkin)
The shapes that he drank coffee with
Exemplified this forceful myth.
The talk was steamy as a sauna
And hearts were worn upon each sleeve,
Encouraging you to believe
The Grail was just around the corner
In the bewitching shape of grass,
A guru, or a piece of arse.

The last, of course, is most enticing:
We want to eat and have our cake
And thus we nibble at the icing,
Politely longing to partake.
Such reticence creates an aura,
A novice out of each adorer
And sacred texts which must be read
(Accounting for Tim's *ABZ*).
He was a victim of convictions
Forced upon Nature's masterpiece
By intimations of decease:
So too we all subscribe to fictions
Written, and published, by our hope
That we'll outlive our envelope.

Even the lecture he had been to
Confirmed love's sublimated role.
The lecturer, though he didn't mean to,
Expounded just the rigmarole
To stir a boy's romantic bowels,
Giving the sense of Rimbaud's ''Vowels''.
Alpha to Omega: not odd
The sonnet should end up with God!
It plays with colours like Dumb Crambo,
Contriving to convey a hint
Of the erotic with each tint,
What we expect, perhaps, from Rimbaud.
I'll give a version, somewhat sham
(Since very free), in lipogram.

### 19

"A: swart as Alabama mammas
Aghast at Arrabal's drama, tar,
A Madagascan sans pajamas,
Black mass, and Sagan's dark *cafard*.
E: perfect teeth, sheets, eggs, tents, cheeses,
Endless Decembers, new deep-freezes.
I: vivid tiling, prickling hips,
Lightning in Spring, pink smiling lips.
U: just cut turf (smug thumbs-up suburb),
Burst thumb (such pus), bush's plump bud,
Sputum (lung's mucus), tumulus, cud,
Fungus, butt's scum, surf's rush, surf's hubbub,
O: ghosts, ohms (off/on), porno book,
Photo-room's glow or God's cool look."


### 20

Perhaps I've lost you here. Well, never
Mind. If it really made you blench
At least give marks to the endeavour
And hurry quickly to the French.
You'll see then what I thought essential,
Considering the low potential
Of closely rhymed tetrameters.
The rest is silly, but it serves.
From head to tail a girl's suggested:
Fetichistic tresses; how
The pavilioned splendour of the brow
Shades a hard mouth; the double-breasted
Pastures where a man might graze;
The *petit trou* in metaphrase.

One kind of girl Tim met completed
This picture of inanity,
Their talk, but not their senses, heated,
Their ideas, not their actions, free.
Their sublimation meant adoring
Tied like a dinghy to its mooring.
A dance was "perfectly divine",
Which meant the men were cool, the wine
A good deal cooler and the rhythm
Hot. Safest in art, they froze
In all the postures of the rose,
But there was nothing doing with them.
"Perfectly divine"–how odd!
A party was their flawless God.

Others had burned bra *and* bikini,
Tending to deprecate the bust.
In garish dresses by Fratini
They warmed their ankles and men's lust,
Or claimed the female was a martyr
Through being brainwashed by "pink data"
And that the best way to be dressed
Was in frayed jeans and Woolworth vest.
With minds made up (but not their faces)
They had men squirming at their whim
(And that, I fear, included Tim)
Of offering in public places
The bouncing cheques of a desire
To light the blue paper and retire.

But Tim had left his latest lecture,
As I've already said, his mind
Aflame with sexual conjecture.
You're right: it would be too unkind
To itemize his actual progress
With every sort of highbrow ogress
Who haunted the academy.
It must be done in simile.
Sublime as jokes by Arthur Askey,
Secret as Open Scholarships,
As frequent as the sun's eclipse
And prompt as Fischer meeting Spassky,
His assignations were not bold
And left him (and his partner) cold.


24

Now such emotional immunity
Unleashed a hunger for dis-ease.
Each face became an opportunity
Where eyes could test their power to please,
Glance up from unread book and wander,
Noting which of the blondes were blonder,
Between each sip look gravely round
As if no beauty could give ground
With tacit promise of contagion,
As if no exploit of the flesh
Could tangle him within its mesh
Or be a quest he could engage in,
As if to life he felt he ought
To offer nothing but deep thought.

Ah, self-delusion! Common error
That in the sum of human kinds
Provides wrong answers! A sort of terror
The unsuspecting hero finds
To come from within himself, a spectre
Using the psyche as reflector.
But just as signs rely on posts
My verse needs characters, not ghosts:
By luck, one sitting near his table
Watched Tim with patience somewhat like
An aged angler after pike
Or a lost demon from a fable
Needing a soul to be rehoused,
A grave Mephisto stalking Faust.

His face was long and age had hollowed
Away his neck so that you saw
Performance of muscles when he swallowed,
While every movement of the jaw
Like a gaunt preacher's in a chapel
Showed off a monstrous adam's apple.
His eyes and motives were opaque
And frequently he nibbled cake.
The hand to mouth was automatic,
The eyes attentively on Tim,
And all the time the rest of him
(Just like this narrative) was static,
Relaxed as if he had all day
In which to pounce upon his prey.

Manipulators never hurry.
They like a sedentary pace.
Their choice is sometimes arbitrary
Depending on their victim's face,
A safer tie or shirt that's cleaner,
A modesty in his demeanour
That seems to show he might be used
Or propositions not refused.
No need to ask why Tim was chosen.
There's always someone to be caught
As groping arms touch, though unsought,
A fleeing shape that's pinned there frozen,
As will in action must take aim,
Or a statistic someone's name.

"My name is Quancy. You don't know me
But I know you. (May I sit down?
Thank you.) I asked someone to show me
Where one drinks coffee in this town
And here I am, you find me drinking
It! I did so, little thinking
That you'd be here, but it was you
I came to find. Yes, yes, it's true!
I work in A.T.I. Dear Richard,
Your cousin Richard, told me to look
You up. What *is* that curious book?''
Tim blushed, and then began to fidget.
He coughed. He smiled. He dropped a fork.
Did anything in fact but talk.

Quancy was not put off. How little
Responses to one's gambits count!
Enthusiastic, noncommittal,
It matters not, and no amount
Of tactful fencing ever really
Wears an assailant down who clearly
Has it in his mind to stay.
Tim wanted him to go away
And sat there in a hopeful silence
Meditating various crimes
With headlines in the *Camford Times*:
"Man dead in café. Shocking violence.
Expert in Renaissance art
Stabbed with a teaspoon through the heart."

But all to no avail. The chatter
Detained him, powerless, like a spell.
Nothing else much seemed to matter.
The adam's apple rose and fell
And Quancy's cake-strewn conversation
Dominated the occasion:
"You write, I hear? Oh yes, I've seen
Reviews in the student magazine.
Quite a talent for analysis.
We all thought so. I liked the one
On Dali and the visual pun
(Elephants into swans and phalluses
And so on). Yes, we see these things
In London. Genius has wings."

### 31

To reach the very heart of the matter
In words so casual and brief
Shows you how genius can flatter:
Surrealist painting was the chief
Of Tim's few interests. Amazing!
There is a subtle art in praising
Which only demons tend to know
And Quancy knew. As flowers grow
In marshes, so in his conversation
Bloomed all the favourite names: Delvaux,
Man Ray, Max Ernst, de Chirico.
Small details showed his obligation
To Tim's reviews, and his respect.
How could Tim possibly object?

### 32

Indeed, it almost made him curious
To find out more of Quancy's game,
Whose interest could of course be spurious,
Simply a smokescreen. All the same,
Even as he sat and glowered,
Tim saw that Quancy was high-powered
And if not absolutely high,
Someone at least in A.T.I.
Who might assist him with employment—
For undergraduates a ditch
Not quite the last of ditches which
They don't, though, view with much enjoyment
And which as time goes on they find
They somehow have to bear in mind.

## 33

From it they wage against society
Polite but suicidal war.
Full-scale attack has less propriety
Than quiet infiltration, for
Positions often yield to meekness
And opportunists build on weakness:
The enemy holds every card
And simple victory is hard.
So, those adept at odes to Pyrrha
Send spies into the B.B.C.,
Forsake the Bullingdon and flee
In mufti to the *Daily Mirror*
Where, mastering an alien mode,
They cheer their lagging troops in code.


## 34

Comrades who demonstrate together
Change sleeping-bags for evening dress,
And parlour Trots in Afghan leather
Apply to write for the *Express*;
Swots who are shy and over-solemn
Turn agents for a gossip column;
Shagged socialites begin to search
For openings in the Catholic Church;
The academic Winter Palace
Takes in its annual Bolsheviks;
Plump organ scholars in a fix
Carry a torch for Dirty Alice;
While student poets roll the cues
For readers of the TV News.

The crump of truth was not too distant
For Tim to start to dig *his* trench:
The warning guns sounded insistent
To someone who was reading French,
Since literary information
Doesn't provide a sound vocation.
What *can* one do with Rimbaud as
A special subject, when one has
Annotations interlinear
To show one what the poems mean
And yet, oneself long past eighteen,
Has still to face one's Abyssinia,
Even (the thought was frightening) one's
*Dérèglement de tous les sens?*

So Quancy mentally had ticked him
Off already on his list
Of convert, mortgagor and victim
To Life the great monopolist
Of single lives. Now in this history
Quancy is something of a mystery.
Into Tim's world you've seen him glide,
Sallow, serpentine, bow-tied,
Peripatetic emissary
Of Art Treasures International,
An institution with a pull
Among art-lovers who are very
Rich, but never rest until
Someone has made them richer still.

And there we may as well abandon
Him since his initial bid
Is made. He has a leg to stand on.
So has the story—at least a lid
Which you can open, if you fancy,
To see what more than Tim or Quancy
Can possibly be found inside,
Or what the ensuing pages hide.
The scene is changed. We move to London,
Where we shall meet some others who
Will re-enact their parts for you.
All that they've done must now be undone,
The links that go to make the chain
Be put together once again.

# CHAPTER TWO

## ❧ The Boss ❧

And what's a butterfly? At best,
He's but a caterpillar, drest—*Gay*.

# 1

In a gracious street off Piccadilly,
Just far enough removed from where
The buses roared and newsboys shrilly
Proclaimed the progress of a scare
(A P.M.'s threats of resignation,
The closure of a railway station,
Industrial spying by Japan,
A fall of shares or Princess Anne),
Gracious, that is, but somewhat seedy,
With antique showrooms ("Genuine")
That cads disposed of heirlooms in,
Some cut-price travel for the needy,
Teashops for talk, gowns for the svelte,
And Turkish baths for those who smelled—

# 2

—Seedy, perhaps, but with a cachet
Lent by its Georgian façade,
(A grey and gold, like papier mâché
Quainter for fading, slightly scarred
Like a Van Dyck that one retouches
To heal the canvas in a Duchess),
There lurked the marble and plate-glass
Of A.T.I. It had some class,
Most passers-by would have admitted.
A single oil was easeled in
The window, velvet deep as sin
Unrolled beneath it over fitted
Wilton, Wilton inside and all
Indeed was Wilton, wall to wall.

Across its pile, in pairs, were walking
Four feet expensively encased.
A couple of yards above them, talking,
Two mouths in which cigars were placed
(Whose taste competed with each syllable,
Since throats with smoke or words are fillable:
Tobacco may supply a tale,
But first the teller must exhale).
"You see, Hingeby—", the first was choking,
Oblivious to this rule whereby
No conversations satisfy
When interrupted by his smoking.
"You see, Hingeby—". Again he tried,
And once again the sentence died.

Now Hingeby need concern us little.
Neither'd said much but nonetheless,
Obese, patrician, noncommittal,
Hingeby had spoken much the less.
His eyebrows signalled hidden power
To make whoever failed him cower.
His smile, benevolent and wide,
Contrived to hide what lay inside:
The fangs of a financial viper.
He rolled his cigar from left to right
And right to left, almost alight,
Regular as a windscreen wiper.
It showed that he was listening,
As a clock's tick betrays a spring.

Just listening and waiting. Only
One with a firm sense of the role
Of money to convert the lonely
From frigid hells of self-control
To the blest calm of expectation
Knows how to wait, his compensation
The ripening fruit of all desire,
Life's index creeping ever higher
And dividends of independence
Accruing in the shape of others,
Lawyers, agents, masseurs, mothers,
To dance attention and attendance,
Pleased to be underprivileged,
Given one glimpse of what's gilt-edged.

And Hingeby *was* gilt-edged, his silence
Oozing ingots. That fixed smile
Disguised with gold intrinsic violence
Like a crude barter-system, while
His balding head glowed yellow like an
Ecstatic hermit's on an ikon.
His spectacles were solid gold
(And his impatient eyes were rolled).
Slopes of his chest gave the illusion
Of pinnacled lapels the shade
Of one of the rarer kinds of jade,
Of old Welsh slate, or a contusion.
His cuffs shot pearls, and white gold drew
Rings that his fingers struggled through.

## 7

No wonder people felt diminished,
Fidgeted, mumbled, blushed with shame
And left their sentences unfinished:
"You see, Hingeby–". Always the same,
The reasonable explanation
That suffered an abashed truncation,
Complexion slowly turning puce,
The tongue ashamed of its excuse.
Thus Harold Distimuth, beginning
With perfect credibility,
"You see, Hingeby–", or "Hingeby, you see–",
Was soon reduced to futile grinning,
Wild easing of his collar and
Abandonment of all he'd planned.

## 8

The upshot of the conversation
(If something so one-sided could
Be given such an appellation)
Was to reveal that matters stood
A trifle shakily in areas
You can't afford to find precarious
If, like Harold Distimuth,
Your *raison d'être* is to put
Suggestions to financial giants,
Noughts on the balance-sheet in black,
Customs officials off the track
And everything over on your clients,
Pull the wool and grab the loot
And be, still, Harold Distimuth.

## 9

He could make packets on a Titian
By bribing all the auctioneers.
He'd launch a "limited edition"
Of fairly obvious Vermeers
So lonely thousands spent their savings
On worthless prints they thought engravings
Or found an expensive lithograph
Fetched, when they sold it, only half
Of what they'd paid. He dealt in flowery
Kitsch, posters and Art Nouveau,
Or built up your portfolio
With someone else's L.S. Lowry.
His dealings were pure legerdemain,
His only motive naked gain.

## 10

At A.T.I. itself the gallery
Maintained a reasonable flow
Of cash, enough to pay the salary
Of those who kept it on the go:
Nico, his young assistant; Mary,
Superefficient secretary
Who cooked the books and answered calls
And hung the paintings on the walls;
Quancy for wheeling and for dealing,
In salerooms devious and calm
With legal guile and deathbed charm
When rich art-lovers faced the ceiling;
Old Fredge, who kept the door; and Tim
(No one had found a job for him).

## 11

But there was other money owing
And there were other fees to pay.
Where there is reaping there is sowing
And every dog will have his day,
From specialists in tax-evasion,
Unfriendly experts in persuasion
And all professionals in art
Down to the mere impure-in-heart.
For many bribes were made to tyros:
Perks to restorers, tips for Earls
And necklaces for office girls
Who weren't content with pinching biros
And needed sanctions for their wiles
In lifting confidential files.


## 12

Much went to Hingeby (in his opinion
Not enough) for he was king
And Distimuth simply a minion,
For a time in favour, obliged to bring
Gifts to the gifted, and beholden
To load with gold the already golden.
"You see, Hingeby—". It was a sigh
Laden with doom for A.T.I.,
The unimaginable spectre
Of failure and of Hingeby's frown,
Of the whole venture being closed down
(Or at the least a new director
Replacing Harold Distimuth
And he himself given the boot).

## 13

Well, well. The interview went badly
And Distimuth was in a hole.
Sympathy is required, but sadly
We find that motion of the soul
Frustrated by the man's excessive
Self-esteem. He *was* impressive,
Surely? And Hingeby understood
He'd do much better if he could?
That no one else had finer talents
For all those small artistic crimes
Reported in the *Sunday Times*?
No one a greater sense of balance
Between being cautious and being brisk,
Between inertia and risk?


## 14

Perhaps. But Hingeby left behind him
Distinct disquiet. Nothing was fixed
But Distimuth knew where to find him;
Would he please do so? Soon? He mixed
A double Dutch and vermouth, trying
To hold the bottle steady, sighing.
He took his glasses off and sank
Into a canvas chair. And drank.
Hingeby was gold, but he was leaden.
Life did not glow for him but drained
Him of all colour. Money pained
Him like an ache no drug could deaden.
He had to have it, like a child.
His face was pale. He never smiled.

This master-copy of the Ego
Sported a drooping black moustache
That made him look like an Amigo
From the Sierras in camouflage,
Or if not a bandit not much smarter
Than Marlon Brando as Zapata.
His eyes were drilled beneath his brow
Like open portholes in a prow.
His hair was greasy as *rillettes*
But combed in wings above his ears,
Innocent of the barber's shears.
His jowl was razored by Gillette, a
Swarthy blue (tough bristles win
The daily game of steel and skin).

16

Individualization
Of capital's most common slave
Needs little detailed information.
We know how types like this behave,
Or do we? He certainly did badly
At what was asked of him at Radley
And spent his commission in the Guards
Learning how to shuffle cards.
But did you know he practised judo
And sukiyaki in Gerrard's Cross?
Commuters and salads he could toss
With equal ease. It may seem pseudo
(A black belt in the green belt), but
It helped to minimize the gut.

## 17

Alas, it didn't make him happy,
Nor lovely either. Nor his wife.
Relations were distinctly *frappé*.
Her look was wounding like a knife,
And he was wounded. So he carried
Scars to show that he was married,
Daring the girls he met to wince
Or turn the frog into a prince.
One look? One smile? A hand that snugly
Slipped into his for comfort? It
Was not to be, we must admit.
In every sense he was too ugly.
Unbid-for in the catalogue
Of love, the frog remained a frog.

## 18

"Mary, Mary, come to dinner—
Deploy your power to console
One virile lonely would-be sinner
Crushed by the weight of his drab soul
Who needs to live a little faster,
Who needs a slave to prove he's master,
A quiet accomplice in his task
Of answering what he dare not ask,
The body's single stumping question!
Lead me back gently from the brink!
Restore me, and restore my drink!
Restore the power of suggestion,
Yield me the grandeur of your sex:
*De minimis non curat lex*!"

These words were felt but were unspoken,
The girl in question was unmoved,
The silence in the room unbroken,
His melancholy not improved.
Mary, sublime in her sweet face's
Quite ordinary office graces,
Came in and out with papers and,
Demanding that he set his hand
To various protests and avowals,
Held out her folders for his pen
To scrawl his personal amen,
Oblivious of the silent howls
Of grief and lust that came from him
As he deployed the signing limb.

His eyes were black as two black coffees,
The canine gloom of his moustache
Suiting a kennel not an office,
His breath like something from a marsh.
How could poor Mary be expected
To love a person so dejected,
So bland, acquisitive and grey,
So humourless, so *ennuyé?*
She concentrated on her letters,
The expression on her face quite blank.
She sent the bond and filed the bank,
Calmed creditors and needled debtors.
These missives were superb—*quand même,*
They owed it all to I.B.M.

How can a silent invitation
Make clear that something is afoot?
Such failure of communication
Must be deplored. El Distimuth
Was not a girl's cup of tequila.
She knew him for a double-dealer,
A squeezer of the elbow and
A too-long shaker of the hand.
But did she know how very deeply
He needed now to be redeemed
From being exactly what he seemed,
A man who valued far too cheaply
All that was rare, and held too dear
The vulgar traffic of this sphere?

And would she think it a disaster
If a man's credit balance sank
On her account, or heart beat faster?
No one would notice, to be frank.
She hadn't got a classic figure
(Some of the curves could have been bigger)
And yet she had a certain style,
And little hands and what a smile!
Who knows what longings filled her diary?
For no one's life is what it seems
And poise can be a stage for dreams
Athletic, airborne, lithe and fiery,
Fully designed to compensate
For perfect years of sitting straight.

Now what's your usual daydream, reader?
A useful shape behind a desk
Or something sultry like Aïda,
Mysterious, doomed and statuesque?
Fright-wig and beads? A hint of faerie?
Or sweet umcomplicated Mary?
Suppose you called at A.T.I.
Offhand and unexpectedly
To ask (perhaps) the price of Hockneys:
Which would make you tremble more,
The lightness of your wallet or
The twinkle in her eye? (Knock-knees
Commonly denote restraint,
Whether in front of girls or paint.)


24

Six o'clock. She wondered whether
Her downcast boss would ever go.
Nico and Tim had left together
At half-past five, slowly, although
They'd never been in such a hurry.
Quancy was in the depths of Surrey.
Outside the door she heard a wheeze:
Old Fredge was shuffling with his keys.
Six o'clock. Rub, and the genie
Of all your wishes will appear.
The hour is magic. Freedom's near
And Distimuth and his martini
Not something that you want to stay
And watch. You need to get away.

## 25

Six o'clock. The air seemed scented.
Excitement, working like a yeast
Upon the hurrying crowd, invented
The hurt imaginative Beast
On whose extended palm might settle
The fragile promise of a petal
As in his garden's wilderness
He wandered in a grave *tristesse*,
Uncertain how his hairy power
Might be transformed and so disclose
The healing spectre of the rose.
All London at this darkening hour
Roared in a silent rage to be,
For a night, both maimed and free.

## 26

Experimental gins and tonics
Were being lifted to the lips
Of eager youths and weary chronics,
A few in gulps and some in sips
But all with nausea masked as relish,
For alcohol serves to embellish
The blank walls of the evening
With its sprayed messages that sing
Of love. Out in the dusk, commuters
Scurried along the walls like rats
With leather zips and little hats,
While girls and foreigners, like looters,
Rifled arcades for mugs and packs
Of Nude Bezique and Union Jacks.

Let's leave poor Distimuth contriving
A similar assault upon
Material things. For since Arriving
(The experience of Napoleon
Comes to one's mind) is not a frequent
Conclusion to, nor is it sequent
Upon that enemy of doubt,
The common act of Setting Out,
We may be sure that he will never
Contrive to sober up, relax
And save the day behind our backs.
His Moscow beckons. And his clever
Conspiracy is brewing, though
Softly and elsewhere falls the snow.

# CHAPTER THREE

## 🌿 The Bet 🌿

*Nec sibi cenarum quivis temere arroget artem*—Horace.

## 1

And what of youth? What great decisions
Were quietly being anatomized
And then performed? What bold incisions
Were made in their anaesthetized,
Incurable and sterile futures?
What gaucheries were healed in sutures?
What student skills ready at last
To diagnose the suffering past
(Eager, having learned their lessons,
To wheel the memory that survives
Into a corner of their lives
For a convenient convalescence),
Oblivious of what agonies,
Called out: "The next experience, please!"

## 2

For Tim, the safe imagination
Offered its usual substitute
For every risk of gratification:
It claimed, unwilling to dispute,
The independence of ideas
Whose objectivity must free us
From all responsibility
Of thinking them. And so we see
Friendship frustrated by politeness;
Desire restrained by the sharp tug
Of feared rebuff; the rueful shrug
Of an inevitable triteness
Blunting the spur of sympathy.
It seemed enough simply to be.

The figures in his landscape waited,
Patient, circumambient
And indistinct, all orientated
Towards that effortless event
That held them to its humble centre
While still forbidding them to enter,
Kept them like supers in a play,
Required, with nothing much to say,
To come and go (or to appear to)
While at the forefront of the stage
The hero could with ease engage
At once the spotlights of the theatre
And the rapt audience's applause,
Greeting his modest bows with roars.

A cheering role, but goodness gracious,
Wait a minute! Not so fast!
Isn't this strategy fallacious
Isn't the audience and cast
The *same*? That urge to smile and fidget
When visiting with cousin Richard;
That cool pretence of nonchalance
At Mary's penetrating glance;
That need for instant self-removal
When Quancy looms; that tendency
In conversation to agree—
Dropped cues won't get you the approval
Of actors you upstage, and you've
Got no one else who *can* approve!

## 5

With Nico, Tim for once suspended
All his social terrors. Soon
He found that he had been befriended
When during one long afternoon
Each told the other of frustrations
Aroused by thwarted expectations.
Tim wondered why he had been hired
(When *were* his services required?)
And Nico felt that *his* assistance
Was operating in a void:
They were, in short, underemployed,
And Distimuth preserved his distance
The better (as we know) to cheat
And at the same time be discreet.

## 6

So Quancy said Tim was "a treasure"
Simply for making cups of tea
(Which Fredge did better). He would measure
Attics already measured three
Or even four times since he'd been there.
He wondered what was to be seen there,
But wisely shrugged and held his tongue:
Those attic walls were never hung.
So Nico learned that to assist is
To ask, assuage, assort, assess,
To make a statement to the Press,
To spend an afternoon at Christie's,
Frame the accounts (or prints) to take
To the auditors (or to a sheik).

At this point I can hear your query,
Discreetly framed but deeply felt
(Felt, that is to say, in theory—
As eyes can swim and hearts can melt
As in true sentiment they ought to
Unless, as I suspect, you're bored to
Tears): "If Distimuth's a crook,
Then what of Nico? In our book
He's the Assistant Crook." Not really,
I hasten to assure you. Some
Activities he thought quite rum
But (and I mean this "most sincerely")
Like Carter with the Pentagon
He knew a fifth of what went on.

Nico had welcomed Tim's arrival
Since *two* young men with nothing much
To do might guarantee survival.
(A tyro with a BA! Such
An image-builder wasn't serious,
The motive certainly mysterious
But no more so than many things
Performed by firms whose underlings
Were underprivileged.) He reckoned
He'd been around too long to fire
And Tim was not a chap they'd hire
To take his job. So in the second
Week the friendship was begun
Of twenty-eight with twenty-one.

Nico looked somewhat like a spider,
All arms and legs and hairy-faced.
His pinstriped trousers were much wider
Around the ankle than the waist.
His basement flat in Canonbury
Was painted brown and smelled of curry.
It had no chairs and was equipped
With smoking candles like a crypt,
And lest the darkness constitute a
Danger to the groping guest
There was a light-show which expressed
The feelings of a small computer
In glowing landscapes made of cubes
And portraits of some neon tubes.

This programme would at times illumine
In changing gleams of mauve and green
Activities more purely human
Than those performed by a machine.
The passions novelists call tidal
Welled up before it. Like an idol
It glared upon, yet deigned to bless,
In various stages of undress,
His victims. When he bit a shoulder
It winked some ultra-violet winks,
Beamed at a thigh and when the jinks
Grew higher, fused and began to smoulder
(Except when, rolling on the rug,
The serving priest pulled out the plug).

## 11

Was Nico glum? He was. Small wonder.
What girl of honour genuflects
In front of (or on top, or under)
A Fluorescent god of sex?
Once they would suffer it, once only,
Leaving poor Nico just as lonely.
He sought, and found, but did not keep
(And frequent changes are not cheap).
Tim met them and commiserated:
Such beauties! He was thunderstruck!
It seemed the rottenest of luck
To win the girls yet be frustrated
In your quite reasonable prayers
For more than ephemeral affaires.

## 12

There was the hopeful lady painter
Who thought he'd further her career
(Her appetite grew slowly fainter
And was discovered to be queer);
A poetry-secretariat groupie
Already partially loopy
Heard ''Dead Ewes'' and went insane;
A lonely au-pair fresh from Spain
Turned out to be a week-end tourist.
Widows he tried and divorcées
Who then remarried, a Japanese
Who made love like a manicurist,
A secretary high on hemp,
Another in every sense a temp.

## 13

Then there was this extraordinary
Girl who like an illness moved
Through London. "As a commentary
On a lost text, which might have proved
Divinity to the lapsarian
World, now rouses the grammarian
Only," Tim suggested, "so
Has love become a thing we know
About but do not *know*. Her chemic
Beauty gives men back the text
In its simplicity, perplexed
For ages by an academic
Version of the passion, bred
In the sterile margins of the head."

## 14

"Eyewash!" growled Nico, whose obsession
With that aforesaid pulchritude
Could not contrive its full possession
And did not anyway include
Ingenuous idealization
Of the sort contained in Tim's equation.
"Her body's simply alpha-plus
And her behaviour infamous!
The combination is desirable
For what it promises: the full
Enjoyment of the possible.
A pity the body's not acquirable
On terms to which (or otherwise
We'd try) the likes of us might rise."

## 15

How could an ordinary human
Being play such different roles?
To Tim, an aspect of the Numen;
To Nico, several tempting holes
Concealed with poise about her person.
To Tim, a subject to write verse on;
To Nico, an object of desire
Confined to purchasers in higher
Income groups. Of course, the feeling
Was much the same: they were harpooned
By their obsession, and the wound
Showed little sign of quickly healing.
In seas of rage they thrashed about,
One lickerish and one devout.


## 16

What of their friendship? Its survival
In such conditions was assured.
Each thought the other not a rival
But a fellow-sufferer to be cured.
What was the cure? A valid question.
You swallow pills for indigestion
And pack a boil with soothing lint
Or a cracked arm into a splint:
The cure is easy to discover.
Can you be sure that aching hearts
Are *quite* relieved by other parts?
That love's achieved by being a *lover*?
Both so believed, denying hence
Their several experience.

## 17

For Tim was still the grave idealist
And consummation all he lacked,
While Nico in his role as realist
Was ever hopeful of the act
That always let him down so badly.
Reader, do not view this sadly.
Only the direst misanthrope
Conducts his life without such hope.
Don't we all feel that somewhere waiting
Upon us is our destiny?
A choice or act to set us free?
Some think they find it meditating
On Skiddaw or in discothèques,
While some discover it in sex.

## 18

You may have seen the girl in question,
Mistaking her for other girls
Whose lidded eyes held no suggestion
Of vague derangement and whose curls
When shaken out failed to astound you
With thoughts of hair being all around you,
Whose legs looked merely like supports,
Designed for dancing or for sports,
Inclined to kick, or strut, or dangle,
Not strangely move as though her path
Were mapped by Venus at her bath,
The hip relaxing at an angle
For whose delight in the effect
We praise its fleshly architect.

"That girl" was how they came to know her.
Smiling at parties, glasses full,
They felt themselves so far below her,
Felt her so unavailable,
That they would smirk and blush and stammer,
Rating a social beta-gamma
Until some hugh with cleaner cuffs
Came and completed their rebuffs
By talking her away. Impressive
Stomachs cornered her. An arm
Held out with confidence and charm,
Partly polite, partly possessive,
Demanded her. And yet, alone,
She walked and smiled and was her own.


20

And now, I think, you may find apt a
Small reminder that we last
Saw Nico in the previous chapter
Around five-thirty sneaking past
The room in which his poor superior
Distimuth was feeling wearier
Than he had ever felt before,
Sneaking away through the front door
No less, with Tim in tow. Starvation
Becomes a serious threat to those
To whom the gourmet guides propose
Their rosettes and discrimination
Whenever a curtailed cocktail hour
Shortens the time left to devour.

## 21

Six o'clock. I have already,
If you remember, logged its mood,
This moment of the evening heady
With expectation and imbued
With appetite. It is sufficient
To remind you how we are conditioned:
The hour is struck, and in a wink
The middle-classes pour a drink.
And if by chance the next hour passes
In light and profitable chat
Extolling this and damning that,
Swirling the ice in empty glasses,
It will be time, it will be time
(I won't say "dine": it doesn't rhyme).

## 22

Now Tim, of course, was a beginner
And Nico seven years ahead
In the art of hunting out a dinner
Worth what you pay for it. They fed
In grills with plastic chandeliers
Or little dock-side trattorias
Or anywhere where instant fame
Had not corrupted a good name.
You know those fashionable places
Where it's imperative to book
But no one has the time to cook,
Which welcome all the well-known faces,
Attempt to hide the *table d'hôte*
And charge for hanging up your coat.

Pretensions wholly self-defeating
Most restaurants carry off with verve.
We suffer in the cause of eating
More agonies than we deserve.
We pay the earth for each warm squirmy
Display of kitchen taxidermy,
Fermented secretions of the cow,
Dissected birds, parts of a sow
Or smaller slices of its babies.
These days there's greater virtue in
Native simplicity, less sin
In hedgerow lore like Richard Mabey's
When only berries pass our lips
And gourmets change from ribs to hips.

Come with me, then, to *Adam's Palate*
And eat as our nude forebears did.
Mangold soup and groundsel salad
Will only set you back three quid.
And those who don't mind little creatures
May dine at *Romany's* which features
Campfire Soup and Poacher's Grill
With fiddling thrown in (the bill
Not least). It says in Egon Ronay:
"It's better (if you have the heart)
To venture to the *à la carte*:
Hedgehog in Clay, or Throttled Coney.
Try Towpath Pudding (enough for four).
It's only two pounds fifty more."

And then *The Trenchermen of Harlech*
Offers the cooking of the Celts:
Amazing how a squeeze of garlic
Improves the champ and skewered melts.
It's easy to digest the nettle
Provided it has time to settle,
And all the most nutritious parts
Of animals, like lights and hearts
And various glands, are, so they tell us,
By far the cheapest. Not so here.
In fact you'll find them very dear.
The management is always zealous
To charge for its civility
(And then some more, for V.A.T.).

But still, I can't pretend this sort of
Thing was quite their line. In fact
The macrobiotic was still unthought of.
The regional and ethnic lacked
Such desperate and wholly gruesome
Embodiment. Our hungry twosome
Made for a place called *Albert's*, where
A fillet could be ordered rare
And be so, where you found fresh spinach,
A whole blue Wensleydale with lots
Of celery, some little pots
Of sticky chocolate mousse to finish,
And sometimes, for the regulars,
Ten-year-old Léoville-Lascases.

There the debate, renewed with fervour,
Took on a more dramatic turn.
It might have seemed to an observer
That some grave topic of concern
Engrossed the pair, they looked so solemn.
What could it be? A daily column
Exposing gaffes with snorts of prose
Was not more urgent, medicos
About an ulcer less divided.
Now most dilemmas of that ilk
(Whether to cure by knife or milk)
Inevitably *are* two-sided:
Shall it be bold incisiveness
Or a more leisurely address?

In short, the issue reached such major
Importance in their lives that they
Resolved forthwith to have a wager
About which means would win the day.
Agreed upon the diagnosis,
They differed on the strength of doses
Needed to bring the patient round,
And here their difference was profound.
"That girl," claimed Nico, "like all others,
Would fall to any seducer who
Has both the urge and wit to woo.
They have the example of their mothers
To show them that the act is not
Apocryphal: they *were* begot."

### 29

He was for showing her no mercy,
Only the weapon of his choice.
Tim's counter in the controversy
Was to propose the human voice
As being much the more convincing:
Not only nicer, but evincing
All the substantial qualities
Of what our noble species is;
Agent of body, mind and spirit;
The passions' representative,
Singularly moved to give
Them shape. What neutral ear could hear it
And not for certain recognize
Their sweet rhetorical disguise?

### 30

A bet it was, then, a cool fifty
(More than they could afford, but then
Nico was reckless, Tim was thrifty
And both as single gentlemen
Might risk behaving like Edwardians
With gestures to a hidden audience
Or, as the claret reached their toes,
A pair of Restoration beaux
Who dally in a world of whoredom
To prove that vice is exquisite
For those with manners and the wit
To hide its cost and utter boredom).
Certain that he'd clear the bet,
Each thought the other in his debt.

# CHAPTER FOUR

## 🪶 The Bid 🪶

*Unde sit quod plus delectatur homo in sensu tactus quo servatur species eiys, quam in sensu gustus quo conservatur individuum*—Fortescue.

## 1

No sooner was the bet decided
Than one of those events occurred
Which make one think that life is guided
By some strange force, unseen, unheard,
That finds it passably amusing
To make what happens seem confusing
And organizes these events
Into a giant coincidence.
Tim was choosing from the trolley
And happened to glance up: outside
The restaurant he saw there glide
An ancient taxi in a jolly
Colour resembling cherry jam.
It looked just like a lacquered pram.

## 2

From one side stepped six feet of flannel
Wearing a sneer that opened in
A blank face like a secret panel
Leading nowhere, and a chin
Like a worn step. From the other
Fell one who might have been his brother,
Sporting a blazer and cravat
And a strange curly kind of hat,
Gasping with laughter. Together moving
Like badly-rehearsed comedians
They opened the rear door. At once,
In a manner faintly disapproving,
Giving her skirt a little swirl,
Out stepped, pale and aloof, "that girl".

The diners goggled as she entered,
Flanked by the Blazer and the Sneer.
Everyone's attention centered
Upon the girl as she came near.
Forks were raised with roasted meat on
That cooled before it could be eaten;
Sorbet melted in the spoon;
Noodles, missing the mouth, were strewn
On neighbours' laps; some men, unable
To stop themselves from turning round,
Tipping their chairs, became spellbound
And had to hold on to the table
To stop themselves from falling. All
The restaurant was in her thrall.

A word from Blazer and a waiter
Showed them into a darkened booth.
''The menu, sir?'' ''We'll see it later,''
Replied the Sneer. His voice was smooth
As eggs. He gave a common glottal
Catch (a cough): ''Bring us a bottle
Of something cold with bubbles in.
And make damned sure it's genuine.''
He ended with some imprecation
Better left unrepeated, then
He briefly smiled, and sneered again.
That done, a buzz of conversation
Broke out at once on every side
As suddenly as it had died.

## 5

"Isn't that . . .?" "Yes, it is, it's Polly . . ."
"Polly who?" "I know her face."
"Not Polly Passenger?" "Yes." "Golly!"
"What's she doing in this place?"
"I can't imagine." "She likes slumming."
"Don't you find her dress becoming?"
"Yes, what there is of it." "Is that
Prince Charles wearing the little hat?"
"What's the car?" "It's a De Soto."
"No, it's a taxi." "It's superb!"
"I see they've parked it on the kerb."
"Is someone going to take a photo?"
"I hope not. Is my collar straight?"
"I must be looking overweight."


## 6

Picture the girl: her hair was Goya's,
Out of which her forehead blazed
Like light. Her eyes, those dark destroyers,
Like a Modigliani gazed
You into a trance. How to respond? You
Pleased her by finding it beyond you.
Amused to see your gauche dismay,
She narrowed them, and turned away.
Slender nose, a little slanted,
Ears the unfolding of a rose,
Neck and shoulders in a pose
Gainsborough would have gladly painted:
Every feature in its place,
Rhyming the poem of her face.

What a feat of contemporaneity!
Nico and Tim were riveted
At this appearance of their deity.
Upon their plates the food lay dead
(The bill however was alive: a
Little murder with a fiver,
Six singles and a noisy mound
Of trouser-heated change was found
To be required by the sadistic
Waiter who straightened out the warps
And bore away the paper corpse,
Which leaves me with the final distich,
No time for more, a good pretext
To move on quickly to the next).

How to get rid of Sneer and Blazer?
How *could* she sit with those two twits?
What gallant action might amaze her?
Flowers? A duel? Fainting fits?
Leaping upon the table? Jocular
And knowing grimaces monocular
(i.e. winks)? Such thoughts flashed through
Our heroes' minds in swift review
And left them glum. It seemed that little
Could be accomplished there and then.
They felt a bit like jurymen
Who should have stuck out for acquittal
But played it safe and acquiesced
And voted ''Guilty'' with the rest.

But even cowards get their chances,
Like M.P.s waiting to be bribed
Or girls with platform shoes at dances.
The twits in question had imbibed
A good deal of the harry lifters
Which sinks down to the bladder swift as
A Bentley's petrol gauge, a leak,
Or mercury after the week
Of regulation English summer.
That's what happens when you drink:
Without a bladder made of zinc
(Which sadly the Celestial Plumber
Struck off the specification) you
At times like these must find a loo.

Which Sneer and Blazer did, upsetting
A chair or two on stumbling out.
"Now's our chance," hissed Nico, getting
Up from the table. "The first bout
Begins! Keep calm, my boy, and follow
Me." Tim stayed behind to swallow
The last dampness of claret in
His empty glass and square his chin.
He then felt ready for whatever
Nico might have in mind. He took
His bearings but he did not look
To see where Nico'd gone. He never
Noticed till too late that he
Had gone not to Polly but to pee.

This left Tim moving irrevocably
Towards her table, where she sat
Watching the waiter pour the bubbly,
While Nico was already at
The gents. He clearly saw his mission
As dealing with the opposition
Before he moved in for the kill.
A hopeless prospect that, but still,
Isn't it true that life is action?
Well, he had acted. Whereas Tim,
In reflex like a second limb,
Proved the power of attraction,
The area of error and
The vagaries of chance's hand.


12

As for his own, it was extended
Uncertainly towards a chair
At Polly's table. He intended,
Smiling, careless and debonair,
To grasp its back. And this intention
Itself (I hardly need to mention)
Was something he proposed anon
To make a firm decision on.
At least, he felt the said proposal
Was something to be considered in
The circumstances, well within
The powers he found at his disposal,
If only he had time to *think*
(Perhaps with something more to drink).

## 13

The gap between him and the table
Became a narrow chasm whose
Dim dizzying depths left him unstable,
The carpet rose to meet his shoes
And bore his weight without volition,
His fingers shrank from their petition
As from a bowl of worms. The chair,
Though getting nearer, was not there
But in a timeless limbo, swelling
Inside his head to monstrous size.
He felt upon him all the eyes
Of diners, silently compelling
Him to trip. He wished they'd look
The other way. His fingers shook.

## 14

Now Nico meanwhile had discovered
Something that he'd not bargained for.
As yet he scarcely had recovered
From the strange shock of what he saw
Or rather didn't see. What was it?
What sounds emerging from the closet
Brought to his ears with muffled force
Yet unequivocally, like Morse,
Their obscene message? Flabbergasted.
Nico continued to pretend
To wash his hands. When would it end?
He was amazed how long it lasted!
How shameless and how public were
The passions nothing could deter!

The drab convenience of a cottage
Will suit a love that's not sublime.
The hidden scrabblings and frottage
Signalled an act there's always time
To bring off and stay undetected,
Even (as now) drunk and expected.
The memoirs of the great are full
Of the quick grope and lightning pull
In the unlikeliest of places.
"Hang on a mo," the boys would cry
And off they'd beetle. Friends would sigh
And wait for them to show their paces
In corridors of trains, on stairs,
With waiters and commissionaires.

16

Sunday leaders still remember
That Honourable Member who
Stood for—well, any *other* member.
Divisions found him in the loo
(Though he obeyed the Whip's instructions,
Was politic in his seductions
And thus paired-off). Gossip recalls
An editor with restless balls
Whose quest for talent for his organ
Led him to many a writer chum
Whose claim to fame was that his bum
Had once been lightly cupped by Morgan
Forster, whose bum in turn, &c . . .
He printed nothing by a hetero.

Nico's thinking changed direction:
If Polly, waiting thus, was not
Therefore their object of affection
(Which seemed to be each other) what
Could they be doing with her? Or she with
Them? They weren't so nice to be with.
He dried his hands and rapped upon
The door: ''All right!'' he said. ''You've one
Minute precisely! D. C. Vincent
Of the Metropolitan Police
(Vice Squad). I must insist you cease
What you are doing upon this instant.
We've organized a general purge.
Adjust your clothing and emerge.''

He paused and listened. All was silent
(Save for the muffled swearing of the chef:
The wall was thick, but he was violent
And several of the waiters deaf).
So far so good. His task was lightened
If they were genuinely frightened.
He issued orders, then went out
And stamped importantly about.
No sound emerged except a hiccough
(What else is there to say when caught?
''Officer, I was taken short''?
''Here's for your trouble''? ''That's no pick-up,
That's my nurse. Victim of strokes
Require assistance in the cloaks''?).

Nico nipped back and softly muttered
In a foreign accent through the door
(The words were welcome that he uttered):
"Here! I tell you! I want no more
This sort of trouble, understand?
The man-police, he with his panda
Car on walky-talk. Believe
Me, it is safe now if you leave,
But turn right, back door through the kitchen."
Nico's instructions were obeyed
In double-time. The escapade
Concluded with a scamper which in
Ten seconds smashed ten glasses, shook
Sugar from shelves and scorched a cook.

The twits, too conscious of their folly,
Weren't drunk enough not to be scared:
Their swift abandonment of Polly
Showed Nico just how much they cared
About (a) her, and (b) theirs truly.
So, deprecating such unruly
Manners as the pair betrayed,
And with a little smile, he made
For the restaurant proper, hardly thinking
Of what his friend had meanwhile been
Engaged upon. But in the din
Of conversation, laughter, drinking,
He once more turned his mind to Tim
And what might have become of him.

## 21

Time is accustomed to the failure
Of real events to alter her.
They merely, like marginalia
On an old text, tend to occur,
A comment on corruption, never
For long accepted, like the clever
Solution of a simple crux.
And rarely in the swirling flux
Of time's equivocal dimension
Actions stand out like islands in
The boiling waters, origin
Of cities and all frail hopes. I mention
Such a banality by way
Of making progress by delay.

## 22

For if this chapter feints or lingers
It only mirrors time and her
Caprice. You saw Tim's trembling fingers
About nine stanzas earlier
Reach for the chair at Polly's table:
Surely by now he has been able
To clinch the action? I'm afraid
Not. By no means. All is delayed.
A dreadful stasis settles, crippling
Fingers, story, time and verse.
It couldn't, in terms of pace, be worse.
You'd be much better off with Kipling
Or Samuel Butler or Tom Hood,
Someone who can be understood.

## 23

It's no good saying that I ought to
Know clearly what is going on.
My characters have not been taught to
Accept me as a hanger-on.
They hide their thoughts from me, refusing
To share their hopes or be amusing.
They change their minds or disappear,
Or turn out not to be sincere.
What I would like to happen isn't
As a consequence, you see, what *did*.
Like measuring the pyramid
I've cooked the evidence and listened
At doors. However, let's pretend
This chapter's somehow going to end.

## 24

One way would be if Tim succeeded
In his attempt to grasp that chair
And consequent events proceeded
As if he were as debonair
As such an act implied. His folly
Might reap a strange reward and Polly
Melt for a moment to a smile.
Together they might rise and while
Nico looks on in stupefaction
Go from the restaurant through the night,
A goddess and her acolyte.
Such a solution has its attraction.
And so—the author interferes,
And music thunders in Tim's ears.

The theme was happiness and glory,
The senses were the instruments,
The variation *con amore*
With ostentatious ornaments,
A grave *notturno* elevated
And calmly recapitulated
Through Eliotic labyrinths
Of streets, odours of hyacinths,
And moonlit figures of sleepwalkers
At large in the dead city where
Every perspective led the pair
Past open doorways from which glaucous
Eyeballs stared out as if through the
Lamenting protoplasmic sea.

And everywhere before him drifted
The mocking and elusive shape
Of Polly. As the shadows shifted
She seemed intent on her escape
Yet still beguiling and alluring
Like a magician's doll, ensuring
His bondage to her carapace
And its contrived hypnotic face.
We'll leave them here (Nico pursuing)
Lost in a temporal cul-de-sac.
Shall we now go discreetly back
To see what Quancy has been doing
Somewhat less discreetly? Turn
The page, dear reader. You shall learn.

# CHAPTER FIVE

## ❧ The Bait ❧

But it is pretty to see what money will do—*Pepys*.

## 1

The house called Summershoot stood smugly
Upon the crest of a small hill.
Victorian towers that once were ugly
Were mellowed now—and ugly still.
Its spacious rooms were buried under
Free-standing piles of saleroom plunder:
Here a column, there a bust,
And everywhere an inch of dust,
Mirrors in gold frames staring at you,
Elephants' feet to stumble on,
Armour, a carved harmoniphon,
Dog-irons, a revolving statue.
You found you longed, while standing there,
To get back to the open air.

## 2

Lord Baltrap owed his ancient acres
To dull industrious forebears who
Were foundrymen and boilermakers
Enabling steam to carry to
An ignorant Empire's furthest borders
(In triplicate) its monarch's orders.
Adept at engineering boats,
They turned their skill to getting votes:
Out of the stoke-hole and the steerage
The disenfranchised lent their voice
(The papers hailed "the people's choice")
And when the Palace gave a peerage
Took cuts in wages to donate
(Unwittingly) this large estate.

## 3

A part of it was old. Beneath an
Exterior of Gothic stone
Was smothered an Elizabethan
Heart of brick—but it had grown,
Like everybody's good intentions,
Corrupt with magnificent recensions
Whose heirs delighted in the fake
Like icing on a cardboard cake.
Small wonder that with swingeing taxes
The present Baltrap made the most
Of ways a lord could play the host.
His stately oaks succumbed to axes
And from his car-parks there were tours
(With headphones) of rococo sewers.

## 4

But such a large scale interruption
Was hardly worth the tiny fee.
Better the wages of corruption
(Granted that one's mortality
Was not in any case in question)
As means to unimpaired ingestion
Of tidy sums. And this explains
Why in pursuit of easy gains
The feckless Baltrap, bald and tweedy,
Inevitably overdrawn,
Could here be seen upon his lawn
Perambulating with the weedy
But nattily-suited Quancy. How
They met need not concern us now.

## 5

The late September day was sunny,
Casting deep shadows in the yews.
Quancy was naming sums of money
That Baltrap scarcely could refuse:
Behold the twitching of his whiskers
And popping of his eyes. Hibiscus
Showered its gay confetti on
The pair. They passed a myrmidon
Clipped from a bush who gave his blessing,
And down an aisle of croquet hoops
Flowers in little nodding groups
Acknowledged Baltrap's acquiescing,
While Quancy's adam's apple fell
And rose, like an exultant bell.

## 6

"Who knows," Quancy was heard to murmur,
"What may be found in lofts among
Tea-chests, brass idols made in Burma
(Or Birmingham) and such far-flung
Outposts of culture that were plundered
When your rapacious grandsires thundered
Across the globe, bundles unbroached
Since Queen Victoria approached
Her grand climacteric, &c?
Sit back. Do nothing. I know a man
Perfect in every way. Began
In life an East End shopfront letterer,
Went on to banknotes, but loves art,
Paints the old masters *à la carte*."

## 7

It's true. He did. The chap could dabble
In any period of paint.
His fakes were indistinguishable
From genuine: he'd do a saint
In gold leaf or a whore in charcoal,
Sketches of pets or patriarchal
Desert temptations, Dutch still-lives
Or portraits of the artist's wives
(Or of the artist's aunts or nieces),
Murals of mayors in roomy furs,
Elizabethan miniatures,
Fairy dells or altarpieces.
Give him a bottle or two of scotch,
He'd even tackle the *Night Watch*.


## 8

And when he was completely blotto
And therefore really up to par,
Another cognac saw a Watteau
Or possibly a Fragonard
Take gradual shape beneath his trembling
Brush. On gin he'd do a Memling.
A schnapps tended to make him squint:
Fine for a Dürer aquatint,
While grappa brought on Titian's *Pontius
Pilate washing his hands of Christ,*
A work that wasn't overpriced
Given he did the hands half-conscious
(Though some de Koonings he had sold
Had been completed while out cold).

Quancy could not resist a chuckle
At Baltrap's puzzled, willing face.
He broke a branch of honeysuckle
With which the more easily to chase
The insects from his scented toupee
And lend élan to his wild whoopee
At all the business they'd discussed
Capering round a mouldy bust
Of Priapus (a garden deity
Whose likeness in his evil leer
To Quancy was distinctly queer
And lent an air of simultaneity
Or strange coincidence to what
Was not in fact a garden plot).

"A rape, a rape! His *Rape* will suit us!
We have the painting, provenance
And now—a purchaser!" Arbutus
Scattered at his manic dance
And dutifully lurking servants
Gawped in surprise at their observance
Of what could only be at best
Unusual behaviour in a guest.
Later, when dialling long-distance,
Quancy was calmer and explained
The situation in restrained
Important tones: "Baltrap's resistance,
Never a threat, is overcome!
We have him underneath our thumb!"

From Summershoot to Piccadilly
The G.P.O. provides the means
Whereby two voices, willy-nilly,
May cross through wires and small machines
That link the ear and lips together
Without distraction from the weather.
Sometimes a voice, as voices do,
Will interrupt with: "Are you through?"
And often it can be a trial
Simply to get connected to
The number of the person you
Originally tried to dial.
But this time Quancy clearly put
The gist across to Distimuth.

The gist is really all that's needed.
I've thinned the details here and there,
As from a bed too densely seeded,
To give the leaves a bit of air.
Let's leave them now to grow (a sceptic
Would say my method's not proleptic,
But when the fruit begins to peep
Nature will know the time to reap).
They say that art is imitation,
But what is there to imitate
When characters predict their fate
And hide? Time for the Dedication!
I'm sorry that you've had to wait:
It's 1800 lines too late.

To you, clear-headed, lean, sarcastic
Observer of the Government,
Master of the hudibrastic
And self-styled "poet by accident"
That out of vacant hours not vanity
Took pen and ink to save your sanity,
Happily I dedicate
Each line of this that I relate.
Were civil servants panegyrists;
Poets of low-life, diplomats;
Roisterers, ministers; kings, cats;
I doubt we'd have lugubrious lyrists
Or such dull politics–instead
Rulers would think, writers be read.

But those days won't return. The nation's
Been jilted on its single date
With destiny. This dedication's
Two hundred and fifty *years* too late,
Launched like a bottle from an island
(Or political careers in Thailand)
In desperation. All I want
Is the mere inkling of entente,
Like yours between the Court and tavern.
For you, whose treaty had set free
An era of prosperity,
Preferred a drink to the mind's ravine
And used your happy verse to bless
The science of forgetfulness.

To keep the mind in a good humour
Just like one's wife, was your advice,
Not to dissect it like a tumour,
Gravely examining each slice
For evidence of everlasting
Bliss to come, like quarry-blasting
Inviolate and veinless rock
Or chipping with an alpenstock
To understand the promontory
From which with idle pleasure you
Might simply experience the view.
Well, Mat, it is an ancient story
But one you told extremely well.
Thank you—and *vive la bagatelle!*

16

Poets adore a divertissement:
They are the hooligans of wit
Not intellectual policemen,
And all the poems they commit
Make shocking reading. Every sentence
Is met with gleeful unrepentance.
Most of them are doing time
For loitering with intent to rhyme
Or being found in the possession
Of little sense. Since words began,
A close conspiracy to scan
Has led to many a false confession,
When po-faced readers cock an ear
For what's not meant to be sincere.

## 17

And if one's mood is not inflated
One's budget will be: lengthy verse
Simply by being understated
Must be capacious, like a purse.
Even the leaves on which one scribbles
Grow more expensive, like the sibyl's.
Small margins, now, for deathless myths,
But not for W.H. Smith's.
Better write limericks and qasidas
Upon the backs of envelopes.
You too were broke once when your hopes
(Living in style among ambassadors)
Incurred for an enormous bill
Pure governmental overkill.

## 18

In custody you wrote that salma-
gundi of tetrameters,
Your "loose and hasty scribble" *Alma,*
Which almost no one, it occurs
To me, now reads, the more's the pity,
Although it's cool, relaxed and witty.
On every later poet's fun
With riddle, innuendo, pun
Or idle use of the persona,
You had, let's say, a prior claim
And may yet seize your dated fame,
For time accords a rightful owner
(To whom all property reverts)
The final gift of just desserts.

But dear me, talking of reversion:
When will we get back to the point
We'd reached before this last excursion?
The thinnest slices from a joint
Have the same shape of lean and every
Same slice stops at the bone. A reverie
Departs from some obsession and
Travel's enjoyable unplanned.
And so, please tolerate the notion
Of wearing shackles to be free,
Inconsequentiality
As a vital principle of motion
And all my empiric English pains
To shift these Russian quatorzains.

Which are, to one so handicapped, a
Kind of habit. Let us conclude
This somewhat insubstantial chapter.
We're none of us now in the mood.
For though it's not obligatory
For every verse to tell the story
Some, I expect, are wishing that
There was more narrative, less chat.
Let's stop–and see what's going to happen.
Write cheques too frequently, the bank
Gets shirty. Any water-tank
Will empty if you leave the tap on.
So put this down and take a rest.
Go for a walk. Or get undressed.

## CHAPTER SIX

## ❧ The Breakfast ❦

she gallops night by night
Through lovers' brains, and then they dream of love.
*Shakespeare.*

## 1

Naked is how we come and naked
Is how we dance back to that world
Whose sense is only what we make it
When the still body, tightly curled
In rooted embryonic panic,
Lies like a hostage to titanic
Oblivion-demanding night
While all our spirits carry light
And reason to a strange created
Inner stage where actions are
Disordered, all phenomena
Overdifferentiated
And everything taken to extremes:
I mean, of course, the world of dreams.

## 2

Where now we find the sleeping Mary,
Her profile on the pillow in
Her childhood bed (a solitary
Bottom bunk in origin,
Now somewhat prettified: the other
Was slept in by her younger brother
Two rooms away) and her still brain
Alive in its occult terrain
Where passions act without rehearsal
And the strict will in full control
Tells the mind's cameras to roll
On scenes whose lure is universal
Though they were never looked upon
Save by an audience of one.

3

What did she see? An endless mirror
With figures passing in and out
Of it, and so becoming clearer.
At first each visage was in doubt
And might have been her own, reflected,
But when the melting glass bisected
The blurred insignia of the face
It put the figure in its place
And gave a name to it. On meeting
Within her dream each mirror-shape
Making reflection its escape
She moved her lips in silent greeting,
But naturally no one heard.
The figures passed without a word.


4

The first was corpulent and sinister,
Wearing his eyebrows like a threat:
Walter Retlaw, Tory minister
Who put the country into debt
By pushing with patrician bonhomie
A cut-throat system of economy.
With him was Samuel Leumas who
Appeared a deeper shade of blue
If that were possible, his features
Contracted to a line of pain
Subtended by a weary brain
That also drafted Retlaw's speeches
Where eloquence and hatred joined
In every slogan that he coined.

The two were followed by that solemnest
Of jesters, Graham Maharg, who played
The easy game of being a columnist
Of whom his readers were afraid:
In bed-sits, semis, mews and manses
They cowered at his fads and fancies.
From his front pocket peeped the fine
Orectic bust of Enid Dine,
Her coiffure shiny as a Sheaffer,
Her mouth agape as with the need
To say extempore the Creed
Or take, with grace, a Popish wafer.
Instead, she could be heard to sing
Better-known highlights from *The Ring*.

Then from another (left-hand) pocket
Glared Sir Ron Norris, union boss,
Nostrils like an electric socket
(Though hairy) arguing the toss
At annual negotiations
About industrial relations.
Graham Maharg knew when and where
To animate this puppet-pair.
If short of copy (and even more so
During a national alarm
When comedy could do no harm)
He slipped a hand into each torso
To praise or scorn speech or introit
At festive Blackpool or Bayreuth.

## 7

The mirror yielded further figures:
Escaped industrialist Mark Kram,
The teeth of Eric Cire, the sniggers
Of Sidney Yendis, the pure ham
Of Noël Leon, arch and cosy
Much-travelled Ysobel le Bosy,
Robert Trebor doing time
For little kidnapped Emily Lime,
Lord Droll holding a lighted taper
Beneath his nanny for a joke,
And many more. When Mary woke
She found she'd dreamed the morning paper
Where all put in a daily stint
And acted out their lives in print.

## 8

But still the night was not quite over
And there was one more face to dream.
Like love eluding Casanova,
A radio star, *Enigma*'s theme,
Its actual lineaments were traceless
And in her dream this face was faceless.
The kiss was casual and direct,
Surprising, chaste and circumspect,
Imbued with sadness not surrender
Like the full moon above a hill
That must in time be gone, and will
Perhaps not come again, a tender
Contact and its brief eclipse:
A silencing finger on the lips.

## 9

At which she really woke, a mystery
To her, but not to you, I think,
Who have been following this history
By scanning rows of signs in ink:
The things which tend to make us tenser
Are often struck out by our Censor
Who leaves it to the guilty Id
To hoard the facts it would forbid.
Were you or I to know who kisses
Us in dreams, who chases us
And whom we chase, voluptuous,
Along the edge of precipices,
We might improve our self-esteem
But then, there'd be no need to dream.

## 10

At breakfast all the world lay folded
In black and white against the milk.
Singers sulked and generals scolded
(Those in khaki, these in silk),
Some crooks were jailed for wielding axes
And others for avoiding taxes
While others still were knighted for
Their murdering or avoiding more.
Life thus proclaimed itself, profusely,
To Fairlea Crescent, Number 4,
Where, single and awake once more,
Mary sat down and ate her muesli:
Toothpaste and cereal combined
To put the kissing out of mind.

## 11

"Mary, *have* an egg," her mother
Pleaded. "Look, there's one just done."
John said: "I wouldn't mind another.
I can't keep up my strength on one."
Every family's breakfast chatter
Is much the same: it doesn't matter,
And working girls have other things,
From hard facts to imaginings,
To think about. Her present worry,
Her cross, dead loss and albatross,
Involved attention from her boss:
"Sorry, Mum, I've got to hurry.
Mr Distimuth said he
Would very kindly call for me."


## 12

"Hallo, hallo," said John. "What's cooking?
Lifts to the office in his car?
Pity he isn't better-looking,
Or aren't you so particular?"
"John, that's enough," his mother chided.
"Finish your toast. Your tie's lop-sided.
And look: it's nearly ten past eight.
Get on with it or you'll be late."
Being a widow in East Pinner
She didn't mention Distimuth,
Fearing that something was afoot
Beginning with lifts, moving to dinner
And after-dinner mints and verse
And after-dinner-something-worse.

And Mary thought so too. They neither
Spoke but moved about the sink
In silent contemplation, either
Washing or drying. What we think
We never speak; in conversation
We never think—dismal equation!
She took the paper to the loo
To do there what she had to do,
And found, somewhere between the Sporting
And City page, a photograph
Clearly designed to make you laugh,
A gem of straight-faced news reporting
Which showed that Polly Passenger
Had danced with a new follower.

Tim's name, of course, was printed slightly
Wrong. The camera caught him on
The hop, grinning, with an unsightly
Lick of hair. His forehead shone.
His posture was, to put it mildly,
Ape-like: bent knees with one arm wildly
Flung, performing the latest dance
With unconcerned extravagance.
(What it was called, I've no idea.
You may supply the name yourself:
"The Hump", "The Limp", "The Curious Elf",
"The Trots", "The New Orleans Brassière",
"The Dalglish Skip", "The Eiderdown",
"The Standing-Still", "The Lord George-Brown".)

## 15

But what the photograph omitted
From its trimmed margins was the glum
And static shape of the outwitted
Nico, still of course Tim's chum
But also now his deadly rival,
Painfully struggling for survival.
He'd had his moments of success,
Acquired that girl's West End address,
Hovered about, and at one juncture
Stepped forward with strange readiness
(When on the kerb in mild distress
She stood before her Fiat's puncture)
To pump the tyre *he* had collapsed
(After some minutes had elapsed).

## 16

That failed to get him in the paper
(Which didn't matter all that much)
Nor in her bed (which did). Each caper
Betrayed a faulty sense of touch
In dealing with love's paraphernalia.
Nico was half in love with failure
While Tim was twice in love with—what?
With youth? with love? but surely not
With Polly Passenger, a person
He could be hardly said to know,
Always half-drunk, the lights too low.
(Remember, when relations worsen,
The friend you are unfriendly with
May not be actual, but a myth).

And Mary's view of Tim, how valid
The Camford graduate grotesque?
Would the reality have tallied
With what she saw across her desk?
The vowels, the smile, the stoop, the shyness,
The knowledge of Plato and Aquinas,
The curious hat bought in Torquay,
Quotations from French poetry:
All these, and more, were blossoms grounded
In roots of personality
Already difficult to see
In nature's soil, so how well-founded
Could be the feelings which required
His playing satyr to her naiad?


18

Feelings which in her dream produced
That soft inevitable kiss
Anonymous and unrestricted
Upon the lips' parenthesis?
For Tim had shown no inclination
To any sort of conversation
(Still less to play it by the book
And start with the old-fashioned look
That shows with tact the way you're leading).
He didn't tease like Nico nor
Was he, like Distimuth, a bore.
It must have been the boy's good breeding
That kept him distant and polite,
Yet he could dance, it seemed, all night!

## 19

And here was Distimuth already
Sounding a fanfare from the street.
She grabbed a scarf, feeling unsteady
Upon her (help, still shoeless!) feet.
"Bye, Mum! Bye, John!" she called out, slipping
Into her green suède brogues and zipping
Her matching green suède shoulder bag
Stitched in dark umber zig by zag
(The bag contained a key, a diary,
Some bijou tampons for the curse,
A tube of mints, a comb, a purse,
A letter warning of the expiry
Of library tickets, a Penguin Jeeves,
Lipstick, and paper handkerchiefs).


## 20

Lashing a girl to bogus leather
Inside pressed steel provides a good
Excuse to be alone together
Since giving lifts, it's understood,
Is kindly meant. Some such idea
Was Distimuth's while changing gear,
Clutching and moving Mary's knee
Gently and absentmindedly
Down into top, thereby revealing
Much more of it than anyone
At A.T.I. had ever begun
To see (though once when she'd been kneeling
With proofs of some new catalogue,
Fredge had peeped in, his eyes agog).

## 21

"Today, my dear, I lunch a client
Who's of great consequence to us,
In Middle-Eastern oil, a giant
Among collectors. Make a fuss
Of this one, won't you? Do it discreetly.
I trust your savoir-faire completely.
I'm having a bit of lunch sent in,
Braised carp and duckling from Tientsin,
Snow peas and noodles, and a bonus
Of baby crab. We'll drink champagne,
Or maybe Corton Charlemagne.
There's still some left. The best coronas
Of course, and coffee as only you
Can make it. That should see us through."


## 22

Lifting eight fingers from the steering
Wheel in unctuous emphasis,
He smiled one of those unendearing
Smiles that require paralysis
Of upper cheek and jaw and narrowing
Of lips: the whole effect was harrowing.
His gaze, intent upon the road
In steely concentration, showed
No kindness, warmth or even pleasure
In the said luncheon he'd rehearsed,
Though as he drove and they conversed,
His hand descended at its leisure,
Patronizing, plump, inert,
To smoothe the folds in Mary's skirt.

Ugh, I can't bear it! Do let's leave them.
Mary can handle him, I'm sure.
As for these lines, it's hard to weave them
Around a scene that's so impure.
I need, in this extravaganza,
Occasionally to give my stanza
A little rest, to let it breathe,
Especially when emotions seethe
Without some corresponding action.
The car was hot, the journey long.
I see no reason to prolong
Her torture for your satisfaction.
You know what Distimuth intends.
His client waits. The chapter ends.

# CHAPTER SEVEN

## ❧ The Bargain ❧

*Nos actions sont comme les bouts-rimés, que chacun fait rapporter à ce qui lui plaît*—La Rochefoucauld.

Time is an index to life's thesis.
Forward and backward stretch the weeks.
We squint in awe at their caprices:
Clusters of hours, the months in cliques,
Dense paragraphing where one reckons
Minutes by inches, pages seconds,
The years alone in heavy type
Like bachelors, with dog and pipe.
Time sidles up when you're not looking,
Pressing your hope into your hands,
Shows you the glossy future, lands
Of exotic promise, checks your booking,
Issues passports, labels, pills,
With the glib tout's deceitful skills.

Before you know it, all is over,
The moment's moving shores recede
And there, unchangeable as Dover,
The past confronts you like a deed.
Did Tim suspect the trouble brewing?
Surely he knew what he was doing?
I mean, of course, not his pursuit
Of love, but what as a recruit
To Quancy's current shady dealings
He found himself required to do.
For Quancy took the canny view
That innocence and finer feelings,
Though almost useless, would in time
Provide a cover for their crime.

## 3

And so we find that it was granted
To whom else but our hero, Tim,
To find the painting that was planted
Expressly to be "found" by him
At Summershoot. He was ecstatic
When searching in a dusty attic
To come across in an old trunk,
With candlesticks and other junk,
Rolled up in paper, a quite sizeable
And battered canvas. Then and there,
Unrolling half of it with care,
He knew at once that recognizable
Grotesque, satiric, volatile
Augustan master's unique style.

## 4

Instant fame in all the headlines!
The papers sent photographers,
Broke up the news, extended deadlines.
*The Times* created such a fuss
That, hot for space, its arts reporter
Had "Court News" made a column shorter,
While Tim, being questioned on *Tonight,*
Found even Robin Day polite.
In all the limelight Tim was modest,
Truthful, factual and concise.
Hard to suspect someone so nice
Who said himself: "You know, the oddest
Thing is that this cornerstone
Of Hogarth's art is quite unknown!"

He told how Baltrap's father, eager
To fill the rooms of Summershoot
With something better than the meagre
Sticks he'd got, went in pursuit
Of heiresses as likely spouses
Who'd bring as dowry ancient houses
Crammed full of varnished paintings, rich
Tapestries, silver and what-not, which
Would give the Baltrap name a flavour
So far lacking. He explained
How such a bride was boldly gained
And just as boldly lost his favour,
How they removed to separate wings,
Apportioning their various things.


6

Baltrap himself confirmed his parents'
Long estrangement and the fact
That with a vengeful proud forbearance
His mother'd never quite unpacked
Some of the spoil she brought when married.
Their whole relationship was arid
Save for the presence of their son
Who found the odds two against one,
And so on. What a dreadful story!
It had, no doubt, some lineaments
Of truth, and served, at all events,
To map that murky territory
Across which scholars, armed, roughshod,
Mile by hard mile would have to plod.

But then, such scholarly geography
Designed to plot a simple route
Is very different from biography
Which needs to settle, not commute.
Baltrap's mother showed small fondness
For his young stubbornness and blondness,
First tearing captive butterflies
Then watching his own salmon rise,
But when he (to be strictly truthful
One should say when his *wife*) produced
A pretty son she was induced
To love this newer gentler youthful
Baltrap. And so they took to one
Another: age and youth had fun.

The tweedy Baltrap grew more tweedy
And more like his rapacious dad,
Became, as fortunes dwindled, greedy
For more than he already had,
And wondered how he could arrive at
Possession of his mother's private
Fortune. She, sensing this, bypassed
Him in her will, and firmly cast
Her by now twenty-year-old grandson
In the absorbing role of heir
To her estate. So debonair,
So idle, so refined, so handsome!
A pity he took his au revoir
By being burned up in a car.

Yes, he was coming from a horse show
(He didn't ride, but liked to look)
And drove his low-slung orange Porsche
Into a lorry he mistook
For open road. So he was swizzled
Out of the fortune, being frizzled.
And all were sad but not surprised
The body wasn't recognized
(Much the best method of departure,
Conveying the personality
With a discreet immediacy,
Swift as a bull's eye from an archer,
Permanent as a foundation stone,
Into dimensions quite unknown).

The painting's provenance, as Quancy
Had exclaimed, was water-tight:
It would have needed necromancy
To bring to the enquiring light
All links the chain contained, each section
Furthering the firm connection
Through family and through bequest,
Through private sale and fastened chest
(Time makes the demonstration fainter
But no less credible for that),
Through patron and through plutocrat
Back to the only source—the painter!
But still, the dangers were untold:
The Hogarth must be quickly sold.

## 11

Just as assassins need usurpers
To lend direction to their skills
And every fabricated purpose
Incontrovertibly fulfils
Existing appetites, so London's
Cosmopolitan abundance
Of all the rich and ignorant
So constituted an affront
To sober taste that men with talents
For rectifying (like Distimuth)
Unfair apportionment of loot
Acted to preserve a balance
Between the rolling and in need,
Between extravagance and greed.


## 12

The latest buyer cultivated
By the precarious Distimuth
(Who for the fake he had created
Needed a shady deal to suit)
Was Lebanese. He'd made his millions
In oil's dark jets and blood's vermilions,
Staining his country's smoking shore
With the materialist décor
So favoured by emergent nations.
Faud Warallah he was called,
Five feet tall, completely bald.
He'd murdered most of his relations
And occupied (plus personnel)
Three floors of the Hyde Park Hotel.

## 13

That lunch you'd heard was in the offing
Took place as planned, a feast at which
The greasy pair enjoyed their scoffing.
The sale went off without a hitch:
Desert hyena bent on culture
And patient mercenary vulture
Bared tooth and talon and ransacked
The stinking carcase of their pact.
At first the sum was hard to swallow
(A brace or two of grouse moors would
Have cost as much, it's understood)
But Quancy's write-up in *Apollo*
As "quintessential English verve"
Restored the snob Warallah's nerve.

## 14

But that's the beauty of the bogus:
It makes us all conspirators
(With knives, perhaps, beneath our togas)
And so light-headed. What else does?
The drunkenness of our pretending
That happiness is never-ending;
Theories of spirit built on dope;
The realist's last and secret hope
That the cold world reflects his prowess
In so conceiving it: all this
And every kind of artifice
Establishes the fault as ours.
Yet still we love it. And that knife
Has been deep in us all our life!

The tongue explores what it has never
Cared to explore before; each hint
From purist critics (who endeavour
To crush all writing) reaches print;
Strikers protest at undermanning;
The ingénue is quietly tanning
Parts you will never look on; books
Exposing the history of crooks
Pay whacking royalties to numbered
Swiss accounts; each girl not kissed
Becomes a female chauvinist;
Litigious husbands, quickly lumbered
With Right of Access, in some pique
Turn into fathers once a week.


16

Driven to the limits of endurance
The senile mayfly promises
To rationalize his life insurance;
The drunk who thinks he's what he says
He is turns into Otto Klemperer
Conducting Gilels in the "Emperor";
The Catholic novelist's receipt
For sex and guilt and self-deceit
Is signed by J.B. Page in vivid
Green; the poetess with legs
As purged of hairs as hard-boiled eggs
Visits the beaming surgeon; livid
Moralists are crucified
By dons who say: "I nearly died!"

The pair shook hands. Cigars were lighted.
Despite himself, poor Distimuth
Showed by his sweat he was excited,
While the squat butcher of Beirut
Remained impassive as a beetle,
His features smooth and bland and foetal.
Within the glass was shifting sand,
Tomorrow and tomorrow and
The day after, the summer shortens,
Bringing the year about our ears,
Fate comes and clicks her little shears
And threads are snipped, of no importance.
If life and works, then why not verse?
Can the next chapter show much worse?

# CHAPTER EIGHT

## 🌿 The Bequest 🌿

Hither the Heroes and the Nymphs resort—*Pope*.

## 1

Oh yes, much worse, for all and sundry.
The weather rarely turns out well,
For when it darkens it gets thundery
And figures in the aquarelle
Splash across pavements hunched and holding
Briefcases over heads or folding
*The Guardian* into makeshift hats.
Commuters, critics, bureaucrats,
Citizens of a busy nation,
With soles of insufficient shoes
As soft and damp as fillets, choose
To make their way to some libation
And as the warming liquors glide
Dry off by getting wet inside.


## 2

In fact it actually *was* raining
The night the Hogarth was displayed:
Lamborghinis aquaplaning
Along from Hyde Park Corner sprayed
Couples already growing chilly
From hailing cabs in Piccadilly,
Late-night shoppers in arcades
Sheltered until they drew the shades,
Those who had left their work were jealous
Of those who hadn't and were dry,
And drinkers kept a weather eye
Open to see if their umbrellas
Still safely glistened by the door
Like some bizarre marine décor.

O alcohol, you know the heart is
(Like cocktails) better for being stirred!
The pubs were publishing, and parties
Imparting, their confident, absurd
Advertisements of cheer. Deception
Lurked in every bland reception,
None more than that at A.T.I.
Where now a livid crumpled sky
Wept over victim after victim
As, shaking raincoats, they advanced,
Smiling and eager to be entranced
(Thus bearing out this stanza's dictum
Which says it doesn't matter who's
Invited if there's lots of booze).

The earliest to come were wealthy,
Their having nowhere else to go.
Only their bank accounts were healthy,
Only their party spirits low.
Deep from a Daimler climbed Lord Wembley,
The first at any such assembly
(Solid as a cornerstone,
His presence guaranteed its tone).
Chairman of every Arts Committee
And arbiter of union strife
He'd left the academic life,
Oozed intellectual self-pity
And offered judgement (as he swirled
His whisky) on the real world.

Then came Sir Peter Hingeby, bringing
An Under-Secretary or two
And, with a naked lapdog clinging
To her, Lady Astarte, who
In her youth had paid to sit for Sargent.
Her withered bosom clinked with argent,
A complement to Hingeby's gold,
Well setting off what she had sold.
There followed company directors
Like Ronald Millions and Les
Scrip who with lies and promises
Had feathered nests (other collectors
Without resource to tax-loss quids
Could never match their reckless bids).

Faud Warallah and his henchmen
Were there, of course. A burly Swede
(Something in glass). A pair of Frenchmen
Who had demolished in their greed
About a tenth of Paris. Buyers,
Collectors, hangers-on and pious
Scions of old families
Who knew what may be somewhere is
(And came to A.T.I. to see it)
Were there that night: who knows what lessons
They might imbibe of deliquescence?
Old Pictures equals Cash. So be it.
(And someone from the Government
Was there to find how much was spent.)

## 7

Then there were guardians of museums
For whom the plenteous spirits harmed
Already much-harmed peritoneums.
A portly publisher was charmed
By girls with orange crewcuts. Scholars
Were overheard to talk of dollars.
Taxis drew up with heated clocks
Debouching doyens of the Box.
Here was Lord "Titian" Gaumont shouting
Friendly abuse at Crispin Swine
The critic who, obese, malign,
Looked ready for a Sunday outing,
With rustic sideburns to his jaws,
A walking-stick and cord plus-fours.

## 8

When Swine took off his wet galoshes
His feet steamed gently in the air
Like vegetables under cloches
Bulging to tuberous growth. The hair
Upon his head grew somewhat sparsely
As, on a ham, a sprig of parsley.
He gave his coat to Fredge to hold
Who brushed politely at the mould
On its lapels. "Good God, man, gently!
I've had that coat since '21.
I got it from Augustus John.
It's worth a great deal!" "Evidently,"
Said Fredge, noting the curious weave
And what remained of the left sleeve.

Together Swine and stately Gaumont
Pressed their way into the throng,
Swine open-mouthed as if a moment
Would see him bursting into song.
The beautiful were there: vivacious
Scented priests made goodness gracious.
Students, unstudious of their looks,
Flashed eyes that were not made for books.
Models in clothes looked melancholy
And some half out of them looked cold.
Nico was laughing, for behold:
He was accompanied by Polly,
Freshly fallen to his snare
When Tim was occupied elsewhere.

But do not think a bedroom drama
Had yet been played between these two.
No shining zip or creased pyjama
Had yet been loosed in earnest. Who
Was known to get that far with Polly?
To act too early would be folly.
The dangers were immense. The bet
Required a cautious etiquette.
So Nico laughed, coolly dispensing
Pale alcohols in glasses from
A tray and moving with aplomb
Among the guests. Of influencing
Events beyond their natural scope
He now had (wisely) little hope.

He gave one glass to Swine, who drank it,
Put the glass aside and walked,
Warm in his purpose like a blanket,
To Harold Distimuth who talked
Apart with Wembley and Warallah.
A rigid smile, unusual pallor
And restless movements of the hand
Gave Distimuth the air of bland
Insouciant terror, paralytic
Greed and vicious wariness
Mixed all together. Nonetheless
He turned to greet the baleful critic
With artifices to appease
An expert who was hard to please.

Swine had spent his life acquainting
Himself and then the world at large
With what was known of British painting.
It was a duty he'd discharge
With glee. He wrote profusely
About the watermarks of Fuseli,
Knew to the week when William Blake
Was running short of crimson lake,
Compiled the authoritative text on
Rowlandson, could date a Dadd
By knowing when the man went mad,
Could tell a Palmer from a sexton
And spotted any kind of fake
Through varnish umber and opaque.

And Distimuth was well-acquainted
With Swine's aforesaid acumen.
The man would know when it was painted
Or, rather, he would work out when
It *wasn't* painted. Not to mention
What clues a little close attention
Could soon uncover in the way
Of technical naïveté.
Why, you may ask, *have* the reception?
Why not let Warallah whisk
The thing away? Avoid the risk
Of such laborious deception
Being, at a stroke, seen through?
Avoid, in short, this hullabaloo?

Of course it all was Faud Warallah's
Fault: he should have lugged his haul
Back to some ministerial palace
To grace a gleaming stucco wall
As yet undoodled on by mortars
Or the bored pencils of reporters.
What Distimuth was never told
When the said fake was being sold,
What during the negotiation
Never a hint of had emerged,
The reason Warallah now had urged
This public show, the explanation
Of his unusual desire
For the great work, will now transpire.

The Hogarth had to be the pivot
Of Lebanese acknowledgement
Of British support: Warallah would *give it*,
Free, to the U.K. Government
In hope that bonds might be unbroken
Or possibly as a minor token
Of friendly ties as yet untied
But likelier now, as nationwide
(Warallah thought) a wave of pleasant
Feelings about the Lebanese,
Replacing earlier unease,
Would surge when news of this great present
Was made in print and on the air,
Catching the people unaware.

So he had just explained, with Wembley
Delighted, squeezing his pudgy arm:
"Magnificent!" But Harold, trembly
And nauseous beneath his calm
Thin smile and sallow heavy-lidded
Gaze, coughed, politely considered
The possible objections, thought
Of none—and knew that he was caught.
For up came Swine to hear Warallah's
Offer: "What's this, Distimuth?"
He cackled. "Are you going to put
It into expert hands? Hell has
No fury like a scholar warned
That weaker colleagues were suborned!"

## 17

What could he say? The critic's talons
Had sunk in deeply, and were sharp.
This Rhadamanthus of the salons
Stood loftily upon the scarp
Of his own judgement. Doubtful pictures
Submitted to his scornful strictures,
In doubt no more, were quickly damned.
Basements of galleries were crammed
With canvases that he'd demoted.
Famous careers at his behest
Were summarily reassessed,
And when his merest qualms were quoted,
Rank upon established rank
Of reputations promptly sank.

## 18

And he already was suspicious
Of Distimuth's elaborate fake!
Would he find out it was factitious?
What grave pronouncement would he make?
The Hogarth, you may guess, was badly
Lit, but who would not have gladly
Wished it much worse? An extra layer
Of varnish? And a silent prayer
That Swine would somehow be distracted,
Impeded by the chattering throng,
Clutch at his throat and fall headlong?
But no, he didn't. How he reacted
May best be told by focusing
Our own attention on the thing.

## 19

The painting showed a painting, firstly,
And next a man without a wig
With arms akimbo, looking cursedly
At what was clearly infra dig:
This painting showed *another* painting
Of a young lady loudly fainting
Amidst a crowd of rakes and flirts
Wearing slight sneers and hooped silk skirts.
This second painting was being painted
By what appeared to be the same
Man who stood outside the frame
As if to disown the girl who'd fainted.
"It's me! But be that as it may,
It's not *by* me!" he seemed to say.

## 20

The canvas was of course quite sizeable,
Being a kind of Chinese box,
The inner subject recognizable
As Antelope's *Leap of the Fox*
(That can't be right, a slip of the fountain
Pen), as Ilex' *Top of the Mountain*?
As Axel Slope's *Slip off the Rock*?
*Lick of the Rope*? *Rip of the Sock*?
*Lack of a Pick*? My wits are failing.
At altitudes like this my luck
Is almost invisible, like Puck.
I'm feeling dizzy. Am I ailing?
All aches and I peep: 's a rip-off, a lark!
Excellent paps! Riper, they'll arc!

Dash it, you must know who I'm after.
He wrote of fools and country seats
(No, not Yeats–there's too much laughter).
He's quite a little chap (not Keats),
More of a classic (no, not Pindar).
His heroine is called Belinda.
(Wait while I pour another glass
And let this silly moment pass.)
She trumped her partner with a singleton
(As you might say) who in a fit
Of amorous inspiration lit
A pyre to put her stolen ringlet on:
Ah, love! What fetishes we use
In the false boast of self-abuse!

Her honour thereby was diminished:
Thus her hysterics, and that bright
Accusing glare (though not quite finished,
Needing a spot of Chinese White
To lend a highlight to the shining
Eyes) and that stretching half-reclining
Pose, a sofa usefully
To hand! The painter, you could see,
Was doing all that he was able
To add fine detail with his brush:
An azure tear, a deeper flush,
A splash of coffee on a table.
For even Hogarth clearly faked
Made other painters look half-baked.

## 23

What are his several contributions,
In ink or pigment, to our art?
Looking at doubtful institutions
(Law or marriage) with that tart
Incisive detail which enables
All sketches to convert to fables.
Making a moral riddle out of sin
He draws a nation gross with gin,
Or in the beer and beef of England
Gives xenophobes the chance to quench
A thirsty fear of the starved French.
Rascals and parsons intermingle and
Thereby betray one origin:
Human nature, which makes us kin.

## 24

But sometimes less than kind. Our critic
Grinned from ear to ear, began
To promulgate his analytic
Hatchet-job. (O ruffian
Of reputations! Grudging growler!
Self-satisfied and hateful howler
Down of doubtful daubs! O fierce
Exposer of spurious portraits, pierce-
r of priceless polychromes, paladin
Of plain unvarnished picturehood!
Under your command they stood
Like mighty djinns before Aladdin:
By others worshipped, but by you
Superbly told what they could do!)

At least, he made a start, parting
His lips and drawing in a breath
(But then, it's always easy starting,
The view more common than the death).
His revelation of corruption
Was subject to an interruption
That no one present could foresee,
Whose unpredictability
Meant that Lord Wembley drenched a waitress
Who dropped her tray on Tim who leapt
On Lady Astarte—all except
A dour young skivvy from the caterers'
Turned from their drinking and their talk
(She went on polishing a fork).

# CHAPTER NINE

## 🌿 The Blame 🌿

So, feel women, not dolls—*Clough.*

## 1

For there upon a little table,
Flashing a fine mascara'd eye
As full of meaning as a label,
Holding her half-full glass up high
Then dropping it, stood who but Polly?
("There's going to be a scene. How jolly,"
Said Gaumont.) Polly's usual poise
Was somewhat countered by the noise
That issued from her lips, viz. screaming:
"The picture isn't yours! It's mine!"
Her mouth became a scornful line
And Nico wondered, was he dreaming?
This girl had been, seconds before,
Frosty, aloof, his paramour.

## 2

Now, like Belinda, she created
And everyone looked on in awe.
Distimuth was fascinated
As by some pale conquistador
Whose sudden presence at an altar
Once made an Aztec's hatchet falter:
Was this, he wondered, a reprieve?
Or was it only make-believe?
Hingeby by now was so suspicious
That he was more or less resigned
To A.T.I.'s imminent wind-
ing up, and with a sudden vicious
Wrench of Distimuth's left arm
He murmured so—with usual charm.

For what tycoon could risk a scandal
And trade for peanuts his good name?
The game was hardly worth the candle
(Nor was the candle worth the game)
And as he watched the writhing Polly
He knew at last the utter folly
Of trusting Distimuth. The girl
Was mad, of course (starting to hurl
Her clothes about) but what a muddle!
Distimuth himself looked lame
(Also for somebody to blame).
Quancy to Nico in a huddle
Muttered beneath his breath: "My dear,
You'll have to get her out of here!"

And yet the scene seemed strangely fated.
"The painting's mine, the painting's mine"
The swaying shape reiterated,
Pale, hypnotic, serpentine,
Like some auditioned songstress destined
For short-lived stardom in the West End,
Insistent shoulders, powdered spine
And voice's low and throaty whine.
Baltrap stepped forward, agitated:
Something about the voice and face
Was far above the commonplace
And made him feel associated
In ways as yet still unexplained
But which were somehow pre-ordained.

And somehow not to be resisted.
But still, such pain! Such *mauvais gout*!
"Not yours to sell!" the voice insisted,
And one white patent-leather shoe
Hit Distimuth upon the forehead
Leaving a really rather horrid
Bruise. What happened then no one
Can now remember, but the fun
Came thick and fast. "Perhaps it's stolen,"
Someone daintily volunteered,
A man whose neat moustache and beard
No bigger than a semi-colon
Was promptly punctuated by
The other shoe as she let fly.

"No longer will I knuckle under
While *he* sells off his precious loot!
The painting's mine, with other plunder
That he's acquired from Summershoot
Left by my grandma!" With this veto
She stayed no longer incognito:
Warallah's henchmen lunged and gripped
Her dress, from which she promptly slipped,
And so they saw the lady vanish.
Her wig was trodden on the floor.
Her clothes lay scattered: through the door
There slipped a figure slight and mannish,
Short-haired, shouldered, epicene,
Eye-lashed, breastless and obscene!

## 7

"I don't believe it! God, it's Percy!"
Breathed Baltrap, as "she" disappeared,
Leaving behind a controversy:
Some people fainted. Others cheered.
An artless few paid court to mammon
And helped themselves to more smoked salmon.
But none were able to agree
On what exactly she or he
Had done or said or why, by aiming
All that abuse, appearing in
Such an extent of cryptic skin,
Throwing his shoes about and claiming
The picture they had come to view
At its much-heralded début.


## 8

"It's Percy!" cried Lord Baltrap, blotting
The tears from his moustache—his grief
And joy left him in shock, garotting
A finger with his handkerchief,
Tight-lipped in the extreme confusion
And breaking of his self-delusion.
Well! After this, could there be more
Surprises? Singly from the door
Polly-Percy's pursuers slowly
Returned: the slippery naked prey
Had managed somehow to get away,
And now attention focused wholly
With awesome disbelief upon
The famous Hogarth—which was gone!

"Oh, no!" groaned Distimuth. One minute
There was a painting in its frame
And now the frame (with nothing in it)
Showed only the dead artist's name:
The canvas had disappeared. "How awful,"
Said Wembley. "Worse than that—unlawful,"
Chuckled the critic, Crispin Swine,
Taking another glass of wine.
"Did no one see it go?" asked Gaumont.
No one had, of course. The air
Was buzzing. Hingeby said: "The affair
Was from the very start ill-omened.
And I consider that the theft
Has *nothing* to do with me." He left.

Distimuth in apoplexy
Sat down on a canapé.
Quancy thought it all quite sexy.
Warallah's men were furious. They
Fingered their guns in silent menace.
Said Gaumont, vaguely: "Once, in Venice
At the Biennale an event
Like this occurred. Some of us went
To open a restored palazzo.
There we were gawping from the bank
Of the Grand Canal: the whole thing sank!
No one knew whom to blame." "It that so?"
Warallah muttered. "Isn't quite the same.
Is fishy. *I* know who to blame."

## 11

Accusation, remonstration,
Loss, discomfiture, surprise:
It hardly bears examination.
We'll tactfully avert our eyes.
For A.T.I. the consequences
Lay not in shame but in expenses
And Baltrap, too, had been outdone
By these strange antics of his son
Who'd claimed his birthright without mercy
(Killing himself the fatted calf).
Why, you may ask, the tender half?
Why Polly Passenger, not Percy?
After the crash, alive, in luck,
He'd tried the part out–and it stuck.


## 12

He had his will without resistance:
To disappear was his one chance
To alter his entire existence,
So he had led them all a dance,
Finding himself more fully human
Living a new life as a woman.
But money, money: who can do
Without it? I can't, nor can you.
And nor could "Polly". He would rather
Reconstitute the gross façade
Of gender, blow the whole charade,
Than stand by weakly while his father
Continued with this rotten swizz
Of selling stuff that should be his.

So said goodbye. And goodbye, ladies,
Goodbye, sirs, and others! Who
If he knows how long his masquerade is
Going to run will see it through?
The man of sense will tiptoe quietly
And close the door on the unsightly
Mess. For here today and gone
Today is perfect oblivion:
No lingering, no lines to garble,
No fidgeting from gloomy friends
Who say, when asked, "It all depends,"
No wit, no worry and no marble,
No tears, no explanations, no
Crescendo on the tremolo.

For shysters are at one with stoics
In fading firmly from a scene
That threatens to require heroics
And battles with the unforeseen.
The lucky yokel flattens ogres
Only because he isn't bogus.
Suffering's for the self-aware
Whose calculation that they dare
Not dare is like the bat's antennae,
Instinctive, automatic, fine,
(Though powered by a high-pitched whine).
In real life there isn't any
Ending that we apprehend,
For when that happens it's the end!

Whenever their accounts are settled
The greatest crooks are not around.
Just when their victims are most nettled
They hold their tongues and go to ground
(Cf. God's lame attempt to straighten
The serpentine career of Satan,
Or Lodovico's to extort
Iago's reasons for his sport).
The same with masters of the phoney
Who never live to face their lies:
Silent are Giordano, Wise
And *Eoanthropus Dawsoni*
(I mean, of course, that Piltdown gang—
Including the orang-utang).

Who loved a girl whose son was christened
Georgette, but wed a girl called George?
Who could not hear but always listened?
Who bored the farrier at his forge
And promised he would live for ever?
Who thought the truth had to be clever?
Who, preaching greed's exhausting price,
Reached forward for another slice?
Who, loving nature, joined the army?
Who filled his pistol full of blanks?
Who changed his dollars into francs
And back again? Who said: "Don't harm me,
I am a poet"? Who, in short,
Hasn't avoided being caught?

Dear reader, surely you have noticed
The quantity of pages left?
The thunder of the anecdotist
Is thereby stolen. Welcome theft!
About the end I'm noncommittal.
Most of my characters have little
Left to live for: Distimuth
You may imagine destitute,
Nico reduced to being taken
By friendly Quancy out to dine
(And on long Shropshire walks with Swine).
Baltrap returned, quite badly shaken,
To Summershoot and in disgust
Bequeathed it to the National Trust.


18

Warallah went and bought the Hayward,
Feeling he'd aimed, perhaps, too low.
The Blazer and the Sneer and wayward
Polly made their escape, although
Their taxi's engine was so sluggish
They were arrested with their luggage
In Lower Bond Street, covering
With stolen canvas Polly's Thing.
("Here, here, what's this? Let's see your driver's
Licence, then. Nowhere to put
It, have you? No? Something's afoot,
That I can see. No, sir, no fivers
Please. If you've done something wrong,
Money won't help. Now come along".)

Mary and Tim became redundant
And time fell ripe into their hands.
The opportunity's abundant,
Beyond these pages, for romance.
Only a realist dismisses
The prospect of some cautious kisses.
But would you have it so? We can't
Be sure without a confidant.
I wasn't there myself. A candid
And exact appraisal's not
Yet possible. I tell you what:
To save you leaving empty-handed,
Let us *suppose* they met again
By chance. And dreamed again. And then . . .